SUNDAY EXPRESS & DAILY EXPRESS
CARTOONS

Tenth Series

A DAILY EXPRESS PUBLICATION

Published by Beaverbrook Newspapers Limited, Fleet Street, London, E.C.4., and printed by Purnell and Sons, Ltd., Paulton (Somerset) and London

3242

4/6

1956
Published by Beaverbrook
Newspapers Ltd.

ANNIGONI and

Annigoni, painter of the most famous portrait of the Queen, says:

"He is wonderful, your Giles. I saw him first four years ago, when I arrived in England. I always look for his cartoons. We now have them reprinted in Italian papers. He is very popular there."

It may seem unlikely that Mr. Annigoni, the eminent painter in the most serious manner, would be amused by Giles, the very English, not-so-serious cartoonist. But Annigoni continues:

"It is a pity that we do not also have cartoonists like Giles. Because he is such a fine artist, such a fine draughtsman, as well as a very funny cartoonist. I appreciate his talent as well as his humour."

"'Now let's do it like the Guards would do it,' I think you said, Colonel."

Annigoni chose the Giles cartoon above as the one that gave him the most pleasure.

"Look here, Sanders—are you watching me or am I watching you?"

Daily Express, Sept. 27th, 1955

"If we opened 365 days a week I expect Modom would still come bowling along at closing time for her reel of cotton."

Daily Express, Oct. 6th, 1955

"And I say unto you, even at this very moment there is one among us

Sunday Express,

whose thoughts turn not from the paths of greed and wickedness."

Oct. 2nd, 1955

"Go on, Fred—

Sunday Express,

slip him off the lead."

Oct. 9th, 1955

"Attention, please, gentlemen. The only cutting we're doing round here today is your 'air."

Daily Express, Oct. 11th, 1955

"I know someone's Chick who'll be going on a charge for Un-American activities."

Daily Express, Oct. 14th, 1955

"Beat us at darts, beat us at shove-ha'penny,

Sunday Express,

beat us at dominoes. . . ."

Oct. 16th, 1955

"Home we go—to the consoling annual commentary on how they don't make cars like they used to."

Daily Express, Oct. 20th, 1955

"Hey, Pete—is this feller behind
any good for car seats?"

Sunday Express, Oct. 23rd, 1955

"Am I to assume that some of us have not heard of Mr. Butler's call for a halt in luxury spending?"

Daily Express, Oct. 25th, 1955

"Remind me to have a word with little Miss Whatsit about her views on the Royal Marriage Act."

Daily Express, Nov. 3rd, 1955

B

"One of his Atom Bangers didn't go off last night, so please can he have his tuppence back?"

Sunday Express, Nov. 6th, 1955

"So much for your economy plan—'We'll-go-out-and-get-a-couple-of-pheasants-instead-
of-paying-through-the-nose-for-a-turkey.'"

Daily Express

"Honey, dancing with these Ivans is O.K.—but calling me 'Comrade' is out."

Daily Express, Nov. 10th, 1955

Scotland Yard is to tighten up security measures.

Sunday Express, Nov. 13th, 1955

"Well—how did your Farmers' Meeting on the Drink-More-Milk campaign go?"

Daily Express, Nov. 15th, 1955

"His insurance claim form will look good—'DESCRIPTION OF VEHICLE . . . Stage coach.
PASSENGER'S OCCUPATION . . . Father Christmas.'"

Sunday Express, Nov. 22nd, 1955

"And who ever heard of Father Christmas getting the afternoon off to go to a football match, may I ask?"

Daily Express, Nov. 29th, 1955

"All these millions they're spending on education make these pipe racks come out
pretty dear Christmas presents."

Daily Express, Dec. 2nd, 1955

Nov. 27th, 1955

Soviet scholars who speak English like Oxford undergraduates want pen-friends in Britain.—Moscow Radio

"Ectually, Ai do faind a bowler hat a trayful nippeigh for the tame of the yeah, Old Boy," said a Moscow scholar who had allowed his Oxford pen-friend to talk him into going the whole hog.

"Before I was reformed, if anyone had told me I'd be on this game for Christmas I'd have nicked his —— ear orf."

Sunday Express, Dec. 4th, 1955

"I thought you told me that George was at the Smithfield this week."

Daily Express, Dec. 6th, 1955

"I've just worked it out—if poor old Chalky takes this pension contributions cut
he'll have less pocket money than us."

Daily Express, Dec. 8th, 1955

"If there's a thing I 'ate it's snow."

Daily Express, Dec. 13th, 1955

"Well, I'll give you one good reason why it's not those doors and let out another thirty thousand of

Sunday Express,

a good place—in ten minutes we're going to open
'em anxious to mingle with the festive crowd."

Dec. 11th, 1955

a

"Yes, Mr. Hogswistle, I *did* cuff your boy yesterday. And if he tips me sixpence for marking his books again I shall repeat the process."

Sunday Express, Dec. 18th, 1955

"Hurry along, Chum, that's just what we need—elephants."

Daily Express, Dec. 21st, 1955

Once again we dedicate our Christmas cartoon to all those spending the holiday in hospital;
safe and sound from the Yuletide hullabaloo going on outside.

Daily Express, Dec. 24th, 1955

"This delegation wishes to register a strong protest about Father Christmases
who come home late and forget to fill our socks."

Sunday Express, Dec. 25th, 1955

"Oh dear—and we haven't even won it yet."

Daily Express, Dec. 29th, 1955

"Mac . . . Sergeant says how do you spell this 'Hogmanay'?"

Sunday Express, Jan. 1st, 1956

"I had a rough idea who'd be doing the yachting if we bought one."

Daily Express, Jan. 6th, 1956

This department, finding nothing very funny in the general news, took the easy way out by simply illustrating the least depressing headline: ARE WE HYPNOTISED BY THE ARTS?

Daily Express, Jan. 12th, 1956

"When they're at school they want to marry a prince, when they leave school they

Sunday Express,

"... want to be a film star, when they're a film star they want to marry a prince. ..."

Jan. 8th, 1956

More troop movements. . . . Turning to the Monte Carlo Rally this week in an effort to avoid military subjects we find there is no escape. At least four gentlemen from the Brigade of Guards and one high-ranking naval officer have joined the competitors. Knowing all about the friendly atmosphere that builds up as the rally grinds on I forecast that jokes like "What have you done with the band?" will be wearing a bit thin by the time they all reach Monte Carlo.

Sunday Express, Jan. 15th, 1956

"RIGHT! That'll be enough good-will messages to Nigeria for to-day."

Daily Express, Jan. 31st, 1956

More trouble brewin' with China . . .

Without wishing to discourage the beautiful Chinese girls who began training in England to be air hostesses between Calcutta, Hong-kong, and Singapore, I forecast that the B.O.A.C. campaign to increase passengers on these routes is doomed from the start.

When all the Mrs. Sahibs get wind of what's going on it's a sure bet that air travel in the Far East will take the biggest nose-dive on record: "Why this sudden craze to take the air, Stanleigh? You'll go by elephant, my lad—you'll be safer."

Sunday Express,

Jan. 22nd, 1956

"If dis chile gets many more scrubbin's there ain't

Sunday Express,

goin' to be enough of dis chile left to shout hooray."

Jan. 29th, 1956

"A few burst pipes and a power cut pack 'em in better'n all the sermons, eh, Vicar?"

Sunday Express, Feb. 5th, 1956

"PLUMBERS' PARADISE," as a well-known newspaper called the week's big thaw.

Daily Express, Feb. 7th, 1956

"Never mind about your M.P. who said that children should be allowed to help on the farm
and HIS little boy drives a tractor—Git Off!"

Daily Express, Feb. 9th, 1956

Cupid is a knavish lad—Thus to make poor females mad. (Shakespeare.)

Sunday Express, Feb. 12th, 1956

"All right, MacBurger. I'M watching the senior typist's room."

Sunday Express, Mar. 11th, 1956

"While they're showing Malenkov the power-houses of Britain I wish they'd show him ours."

Daily Express, Mar. 16th, 1956

"Shilling each way Frisky Scot for the Lincolnshire and an even shilling Dr. Fisher doesn't ask Malenkov round for tea."

Sunday Express, Mar. 18th, 1956

"I wonder if our church clock striking fifty-two instead of two has got anything to do with somebody reading about little boys ringing church bells in Cyprus."

Daily Express, Mar. 20th, 1956

"Malik, Malenkov, Serov, Krushchev, Bulganin—if them Russians was to declare war today there'd be half of 'em over here already."

Sunday Express, Mar. 25th, 1956

"What with horses doing the National course twice round without their riders and the Queen Mother's horse wanting to jump over a jump that wasn't there, I feel a bit of a fool."

Daily Express, Mar. 27th, 1956

"Harry, lend me a shilling."

Daily Express, Mar. 31st, 1956

"Hey—you missed one."

Sunday Express, April 1st, 1956

"I dare say I can get the ship cleaned up in time for Grace Kelly's wedding but I can't promise the same thing about the crew."

Daily Express, April 2nd, 1956

"Yet it's *us* they tag 'dirty'."

Daily Express, April 3rd, 1956

"Isn't it wonderful! We're all going to Grace Kelly's wedding."

Daily Express, April 6th, 1956

"Which of these men attended that disgusting strip-tease concert?"

"All right, Major—we'll omit the first line—'Arise! ye starvelings from your slumber . . .'"

Sunday Express, April 15th, 1956

"Grace Kelly's got one thing at her wedding I'm glad I didn't have at mine—you in a top-hat."

Daily Express, April 11th, 1956

dear readers,
~~they're off~~ ~~as the monky said~~

in case you may have missed the occasional anouncments recently that there is a wedding on next week well there is. and mr giles and his famly leave this morning by air for monaco.   some of them had to be frog-marched to the airport and some of them like grace kellys' poodel are traveling in air conditioned kennels including me.

there is no truth in the rumor that mr giles old freind king frouk is meeting us at monty carlo and mr giles editor have made him promise not to take the miky as it is really a very solem occasion with the moon coming up over monaco and no nonsense.

yours truly
giles jun'r. →

pe **s.** . i reckon evryone in monacos a bit jumpy because that eve periks going to the wedding as well
pe pe s. grandma reckons the only reason theyr'e sending grandma is to stop grandma bying mr bulganin and mr kruchshev some drinks.

Daily Express, April 13th, 1956

"That's handy—a whacking great hole in Lady Docker's yacht!"

Daily Express, April 16th, 1956

— BUT MON DIEU! SHE'S LEFT HERS AT HOME.

April 19th, 1956

"Very good, Sergeant—replace bearskins."

Daily Express, April 25th, 1956

"You might like to know that while you've been up at Claridges keeping an eye on Bulganin someone nipped in here and pinched your bike."

Sunday Express, April 29th, 1956

dear comrade mum,

Just a few lines to let you know that I arrived safely and am having a wonderful time.

I must say that this bourgeois, Western style of living suits me down to the ground. Ever since I arrived I have been on the bottle, with unlimited eggs, butter, and milk, and a special private room with bath and attendance at the London Zoo.

         *   *   *   *   *

Daily Express,

On Monday I was taken to Windsor Castle and everybody was very nice, especially a little Corgi named Susan who showed me how to play at biting Grenadier Guards' ankles.

It is a lovely game and easy to play because the Guardsmen are not allowed to bite you back but have to stand very still as if nothing was happening, and only if you are very, very quiet while you are playing can you sometimes hear them say funny little words which I have not learned the meaning of yet.

Comrades Bulganin and Krushchev are also having a wonderful time, but they are not allowed to bite anybody's ankles although quite a lot of people over here have been taking a nip at them, especially some members called Socialists who you would think would rather play another game called Shaking Hands.

Two things I have noticed over here that are different from life at home are—first, that they treat hanging very seriously and run around all day deciding whether they are going to hang one another or not, and second, that nobody seems to work very much except policemen and zoo keepers.

*   *   *   *   *

But, by and large, I think I prefer their decadent way of life to yours, Mother, and I'll see if I can arrange for you, Bruinvitch, Rupertvitch, and sister Olgavitch to be deported from Siberia to Regent's Park.

I must close now as the head keeper has just brought my elevenses—a trough of carrots, sweet-roots, and caviar.

Your loving son,

nikki.

P.S.   Mr. Eden seems a very nice comrade and hasn't taken a nip at Comrades B or K yet.

April 27th, 1956

"Right! Inside, the pair of you."

Daily Express, May 1st, 1956

"Tea money—one and six, Christmas club—five bob, football sweep—one tanner,
holiday savings—another tanner . . ."

Daily Express, May 5th, 1956

Sunday Express, May 6th, 1956

"If ALL of us gave up smoking the gain in man-hours would wipe out the need for Automation."

Daily Express, May 10th, 1956

"It's not the Russians sticking bombs under the ship, sir—only me and Albert coming home a bit late."

Sunday Express, May 13th, 1956

"When they told me I couldn't marry you because you didn't pass the security check,
I thought I'd better tell them you worked here."

Daily Express, May 17th, 1956

F

dear comrade mum,

Just a few more lines to let you know that since my last letter telling you what a wonderful place England is I've changed my mind.

I hope this reaches you in time to stop you, Bruinvitch, Rupertvitch, and sister Olgavitch emigrating from Siberia to Regent's Park as this is no safe place for respectable comrade bears to be.

Apart from free-lance frogmen spying under Bulganin's boat, the whole Zoo is alive with spies and reactionary forces combined to sabotage the peaceful co-existence between U.S.S.R. and Regent's Park.

Only this week top-comrade Pollitt has been placed on the transfer list, and I myself am just recovering from an attempt to remove me from my high office by a Fascist beast who tried to polish me off with an over-ripe banana.

But don't worry about me, Comrade Mum, they won't get away with that one again. Every time my keeper

Daily Express,

brings my meals I try them out first on my stablemate Rusk, who they put in with me under the cloak of friendship and who I now suspect is nothing but a frogman disguised as a little bear.

I first had my suspicions about him when he clouted me one from behind and knocked me for six off my swing. I now keep that son of a Ruskoyavitch in front of me where I can see him.

They haven't let me go to Windsor Castle any more since I wrote to you, and I hear that Susan the Corgi, who lodges there, was given a brain-washing after my visit. Not that there was anything that I could teach her. In fact, as I told you before, it was *she* who taught *me* a thing or two—like biting Guardsmen's ankles, for instance.

I think Mele-Kush, the Cossack stallion that was given to Comrade Duke of Edinburgh by Comrades Bulganin and Krushchev, must have been over the castle recently and taken a lesson from Susan, because I read in Sunday's paper that he took a nip at one of his grooms.

Well done, Mele-Kush.

I am now waiting to hear that Zamon, the other horse which was given to Prince Charles, has got cracking on his grooms with those hind feet of his.

I will close now as the head keeper is running my bath with his back towards me within easy swiping distance. We'll teach 'em a few normal courtesies before we've finished.

Your loving son,

P.S. Is it true that Moscow has announced that Mele-Kush's nip at his groom took place "without official permission" of the Kremlin?

P.P.S. *Pravda* certainly gave that Gaitskell feller the old what-o, didn't they?

May 15th, 1956

"I'm off duty in ten minutes, when I shall show Davy Crockett here who's King of the Wild Frontier."

Sunday Express, May 20th, 1956

"O.K., MacElroy—let's not get too many jumps ahead with this co-existence."

Sunday Express, May 27th, 1956

"Do it himself, indeed!"

"We're not exactly refugees *from* Egypt, madam—we were on our way there for a holiday."

Sunday Express

"Guess we was ambushed by a bunch of goldarn limeys who have gotten themselves over the border in our apparel."

Daily Express, May 29th, 1956

National Safety Campaign No. 1.

Daily Express, May 31st, 1956

National Safety Campaign No. 2.

Daily Express, June 2nd, 1956

National Safety Campaign No. 3.

Daily Express, June 6th, 1956

National Safety Campaign No. 4.

Thanks to the great success of the Giles SAFETY IN THE HOME campaign it is now possible to obtain the new "SAFETY-BELT" (*illustrated here*) at all leading stores.

Made of extra-toughened steel, it can be bought in easily assembled sections joined with simple locking nuts, or welded together for good and all time.

The de luxe model is designed to plug into A/C or D/C mains for added protection, and can be supplied lined with barbed wire at slightly extra cost.

Besides keeping your child away from the many danger zones around the house, such as electric points, fires, workshops, pianos, etc., it has the extra advantage of keeping your child away from you. Cats and dogs appreciate this great feature.

The anti-splash barricades shown here are made to withstand heavy peltings from acorns, bread and milk, spanners, marbles, etc., and are worthwhile extras.

Daily Express, June 8th, 1956

"Show me a Jockey Club rule that says you CAN'T enter an automation horse in the Derby."

Sunday Express, June 3rd, 1956

"We can't all be Pat Smythe, Miss Ringbone."

Sunday Express, June 10th, 1956

"Tch! tch! Your Mayfair outfit's not wearing very well, Comrade."

Daily Express, June 12th, 1956

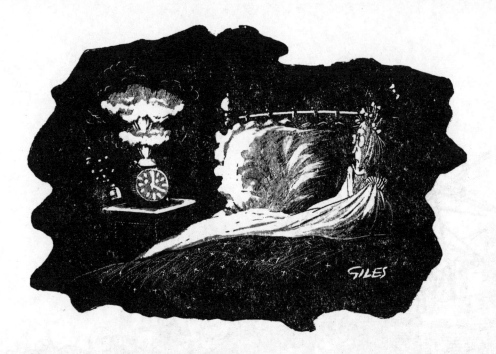

The announcement that luminous clocks and watches produce more radioactivity than H-bombs puts another item on the You'll-get-so-and-so if you eat-smoke-or-have-so-and-so list.

In its search for the best hypochondriac the *Daily Express* is considering* offering as a prize a free and unaccompanied holiday in Monte Bello for the neatest answers to the following questions:

1. What do doctors say you'll get if you smoke eighty-odd cigarettes a day:
   (*a*) A packet? (*b*) C. of the L.? (*c*) Housemaid's knee?

2. What do doctors say you'll catch if you eat: (*a*) Eggs and bacon? (*b*) Anything nice?

3. Which part of your inside will go for a Burton if you drink gin?

4. How much of your gin will go for a Burton if your friends know you've got some?

* Considering.

Daily Express,

5. When did you last see your: (*a*) Doctor? (*b*) Tongue?

6. If your boy comes home covered in spots do you: (*a*) Give him a thick ear?
   (*b*) Give him a horse pill?

7. If you are radioactive can you get: (*a*) Luxembourg? (*b*) A.F.N.?
   Serve you right in any case.

8. Write a five-thousand-word essay on a postcard on "My Funniest Ailment",
   and keep watching this paper for further instructions about where to send it.

June 15th, 1956

"We're coming back Tuesday for Ascot."

Sunday Express, June 17th, 1956

"If Harry Truman's your buddy—WHY can't you get us all tickets for his lunch with the Lord Mayor?"

Daily Express, June 19th, 1956

"Come home, Father—and we'll promise we won't have Wimbledon on the radio
and television all day long for a fortnight."

Daily Express, June 21st, 1956

"Now we'll see which shaves the best—the electric razor or the old-fashioned cut-throat."

Sunday Express, June 24th, 1956

"As that last smashing forehand drive lands in the far corner to bring him victory he leaps nimbly over the net to shake the hand of his opponent—— Oh dear! His toe has just tipped the net . . ."

Daily Express, June 26th, 1956

"I see the price of ammunition's going up, Larry."

Daily Express, June 29th, 1956

"My Grandma says hang everybody."

Daily Express, July 3rd, 1956

"Pass on, Sweetie—I've put my sixpence in your money-box."

Daily Express, July 6th, 1956

"I should take that off your windscreen, Harry."

Sunday Express, July 8th, 1956

"Harry's doing all right. This parking offence is running into its fifth day's hearing."

Daily Express, July 10th, 1956

"Nicked my kisser with my slasher

Sunday Express,

whilst shaving this morning.''

July 22nd, 1956

"Never mind about the NO-HANGING Bill being turned down by the Lords—take that rope off my Ronnie."

Daily Express, July 12th, 1956

"Sorry, lads—you'll have to foot it. They're out in sympathy with the strikers."

Daily Express, July 27th, 1956

"Witness Egghead playing the Intellectual-to-marry-Marilyn Monroe technique."

Sunday Express, July 1st, 1956

"Hey you! Put that cap straight. Third man there—get your hair fixed
Marilyn will be passing this way any minute."

Sunday Express, July 15th, 1956

"Watch the change of temperature when he finds the little bit of news among the Marilyns about Argentina sending more and more beef to England."

Daily Express, July 17th, 1956

DAILY EXPRESS REPORTS NEW CAVE PAINTINGS DISCOVERED IN FRANCE

That there was a Giles 20,000 years ago is encouraging enough. That there was one working is an even greater compliment. But I advise archaeologists to check on the origin of these newly discovered wall paintings. 'Tis less than a year ago that we took the family to France.

Daily Express, July 24th, 1956

"My Harry's a striker on holiday—the other one's his boss who happens to be staying at our hotel."

Daily Express, July 29th, 1956

"Good old Nasser."

Daily Express, July 31st, 1956

"It says: 'We were interested to read that your big drum blew away on parade yesterday. You may remember, some time back, one of our officers fell off his horse and the following morning some joker left a little pot of glue on the guardroom step. We enclose a safety-pin as we wouldn't like to see your big drum blow away in front of Colonel Nasser. . . .   Signed: The Brigade of Guards.' "

Daily Express, August 1st, 1956

"Tell him Nasser held us up in the Canal."

Daily Express, August 3rd, 1956

"Help."

Daily Express, August 5th, 1956

"I'll give you 'Good morning, Nasser' if I come over there."

Daily Express, August 6th, 1956

"Come, O Wide One, the colonel hath need of thee."

Daily Express, August 10th, 1956

"Giving me a cup with no handle and saying 'I hope it chokes you, you blacklegging old scab' ain't forgiving and forgetting, Miss."

Daily Express, August 14th, 1956

"What's this? 'Darling Basilkins, You remember when the feelthy British here was last time well I am still live in the same little house in Cairo if you care to give me a call when you come again yes please, Your own little Cleo.'"

Daily Express, August 16th, 1956

"I hope he gets a move on—the Town kick-off at two-thirty and my ship sails at six."

Sunday Express, August 19th, 1956

"O.K., in she goes."

Daily Express, August 22nd, 1956

The three gentlemen who have been larking about in the Atlantic on a raft
recently are not eligible for this competition.

Daily Express, August 24th, 1956

"I beg to dispute your inexhaustible knowledge of world affairs, but Disraeli was not a famous Australian cricketer in 1864."

Sunday Express, August 26th, 1956